到点啦，麦克斯！

【美】基蒂·理查兹◎著
【美】吉奥雅·法蒙吉◎绘
袁　颖◎译

天津出版传媒集团

新蕾出版社

图书在版编目（CIP）数据

到点啦,麦克斯! /（美）理查兹（Richards,K.）著；（美）法蒙吉（Fiammenghi,G.）
绘；袁颖译.
—天津:新蕾出版社,2014.1(2024.12 重印)
(数学帮帮忙·互动版)
书名原文:It's About Time, Max!
ISBN 978-7-5307-5898-4

Ⅰ.①到…
Ⅱ.①理…②法…③袁…
Ⅲ.①数学–儿童读物
Ⅳ.①O1–49

中国版本图书馆 CIP 数据核字(2013)第 270443 号

It's About Time, Max! by Kitty Richards;
Illustrated by Gioia Fiammenghi.
Copyright ⓒ 2000 by Kane Press, Inc.
All rights reserved, including the right of reproduction in whole or in part in any
form. This edition published by arrangement with Kane Press, Inc. New York, NY,
represented by Lerner Publishing Group through The ChoiceMaker Korea Co.
Agency.
Simplified Chinese translation copyright ⓒ 2014 by New Buds Publishing House
(Tianjin) Limited Company
ALL RIGHTS RESERVED
本书中文简体版专有出版权经由中华版权代理中心授予新蕾出版社(天津)有
限公司。未经许可,不得以任何方式复制或抄袭本书的任何部分。
津图登字:02-2012-224

出版发行:天津出版传媒集团
　　　　　新蕾出版社
http://www.newbuds.com.cn

地　　　址	:天津市和平区西康路 35 号(300051)	
出 版 人	:马玉秀	
电　　　话	:总编办 (022)23332422	
	发行部 (022)23332679　23332351	
传　　　真	:(022)23332422	
经　　　销	:全国新华书店	
印　　　刷	:天津新华印务有限公司	
开　　　本	:787mm×1092mm　1/16	
印　　　张	:3	
版　　　次	:2014 年 1 月第 1 版　2024 年 12 月第 26 次印刷	
定　　　价	:12.00 元	

无处不在的数学

资深编辑 卢 江

人们常说"兴趣是最好的老师",有了兴趣,学习就会变得轻松愉快。数学对于孩子来说或许有些难,因为比起语文,数学显得枯燥、抽象,不容易理解,孩子往往不那么喜欢。可许多家长都知道,学数学对于孩子的成长和今后的生活有多么重要。不仅数学知识很有用,学习数学过程中获得的数学思想和方法更会影响孩子的一生,因为数学素养是构成人基本素质的一个重要因素。但是,怎样才能让孩子对数学产生兴趣呢?怎样才能激发他们兴致勃勃地去探索数学问题呢?我认为,让孩子读些有趣的书或许是不错的选择。读了这套"数学帮帮忙",我立刻产生了想把它们推荐给教师和家长朋友们的愿望,因为这真是一套会让孩子爱上数学的好书!

这套有趣的图书从美国引进,原出版者是美国资深教育专家。每本书讲述一个孩子们生活中的故事,由故事中出现的问题自然地引入一个数学知识,然后通过运用数学知识解决问题。比如,从帮助外婆整理散落的纽扣引出分类,从为小狗记录藏骨头的地点引出空间方位等等。故事素材全部来源于孩子们的真实生活，不是童话，不是幻想，而是鲜活的生活实例。正是这些发生在孩子身边的故事，让孩子们懂得，数学无处不在并且非常有用；这些鲜活的实例也使得抽象的概念更易于理解，更容易激发孩子学习数学的兴趣，让他们逐渐爱上数学。这样的教育思想和方法与我国近年来提倡的数学教育理念是十分吻合的！

这是一套适合 5~8 岁孩子阅读的书，书中的有趣情节和生动的插画可以将抽象的数学问题直观化、形象化，为孩子的思维活动提供具体形象的支持。如果亲子共读的话，家长可以带领孩子推测情节的发展，探讨解决难题的办法，让孩子在愉悦的氛围中学到知识和方法。

值得教师和家长朋友们注意的是，在每本书的后面，出版者还加入了"互动课堂"及"互动练习"，一方面通过一些精心设计的活动让孩子巩固新学到的数学知识，进一步体会知识的含义和实际应用；另一方面帮助家长指导孩子阅读，体会故事中数学之外的道理，逐步提升孩子的阅读理解能力。

我相信孩子读过这套书后一定会明白，原来，数学不是烦恼，不是包袱，数学真能帮大忙！

"该起床啦，麦克斯！"妈妈在叫我。

　　我打着哈欠看了一眼手表，7：00，每天早上我都在这个时候起床，然后在 8：05 赶上校车前把所有该做的事情全部做好。我从来没有迟到过。

7:05—7:15，洗澡。

7:15—7:20，刷牙。

7:20—7:30，穿衣服。

7:30—7:45，吃早饭，香脆的麦片真好吃！

7:45—7:55，去遛狗，他叫"僵尸"。（这是因为我很爱看怪物电影！）

然后我去等校车。校车会在 8:05 到站，司机邓恩太太每天都很准时，跟我一样。

好吧，好吧，我得承认，有一阵子我也会迟到。事情是这样的……

5

"该起床啦，麦克斯！"妈妈在叫我。

我冲了澡刷了牙，穿上衣服，然后去拿我的数字式手表。

表没在床头柜上，没在浴袍口袋里，也没在洗手池边！哦，天哪！

我系好运动鞋，跑下楼去。

"嗨，"我说，"谁看见我的手表了？"

"没有啊。"爸爸妈妈说。

"没有啊。"姐姐安说。

"那我可怎么办啊？"我嘟囔着。

"我有块表，借给你用吧。"安说。

"你最好快点。"妈妈说,"已经7:50了。"

天哪,我比平时晚了5分钟!我戴上安的手表,叫上僵尸,一阵风似的冲出门外。

我们遛到街角时，我决定看下时间。

哎呀！这表不是数字式的，上面有指针！
这是几点啊？我不会看，只好用最快的速度
跑回家。

　　哎哟，妈妈已经在门外等我了，脸色看上去不怎么好。"你误了校车！"她说。

于是，妈妈只好开车送我去学校，还写了张迟到假条。我简直太……太……太无地自容了。

第二天是星期六。我相当兴奋,因为下午我要参加我的首次"惊喜派对"。爸爸会开车送我过去。

他一直在打瞌睡。"万一我睡过了头,记得要在5:30叫醒我。"他说,"我们得那个时间出发。"

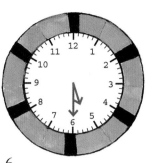

5:30

我盯着爸爸看。我的父母都不赶时髦，家里连一块数字表都没有。

"5:30？"我还真说不好。

"你知道吧，"爸爸说，"就是在长针指到6，短针指到5和6之间的时候？"爸爸笑了。

听起来似乎简单多了。"好的。"我说。

等到短针指到 6，长针指到 5 的时候，我把爸爸叫醒。他不高兴，非常不高兴。

"麦克斯！"他说，"我让你 5:30 叫醒我，可现在都 6:25 了！"

我准是把长短指针搞混了。我们立刻驱车赶到派对现场，可我错过了最精彩环节——大家全都跳起来喊"惊喜"。真倒霉啊！

　　那个周日下午，妈妈和我去看电影。我说过的，我喜欢看怪物电影，妈妈也是。

　　我们到得有些早。

　　"我想去趟杰的漫画书店。"我说，"也许会有新的怪物漫画呢。"

　　"我想去音像店逛逛。"妈妈说，"咱们 3 点 1 刻在这里会合。"

　　"啊……要不，我还是跟你一起去吧。"我说。可我突然想起来，那家漫画书店的墙上有一只很大的电子钟。

　　"好吧。"我说，"就定 3 点 1 刻。"

　　我看了一会儿漫画书。然后等墙上的钟显示
了3点1刻,我起身去和妈妈会合。

"麦克斯,我都等了你10分钟了。"妈妈说,"电影已经开演了!"

　　"可我挺准时的啊。"我说,"3点1刻,一刻钟是25分,现在就是3:25啊。"

　　"不对,麦克斯。"妈妈说,"一小时是60分,一刻钟是15分。3点1刻是3:15,不是3:25。"

　　就这样,我们错过了电影。我感觉糟透了。

那天晚上，妈妈把我叫进客厅。全家人都在，桌上还放了几张画有钟表和数字的纸。

"麦克斯，"妈妈说，"我们必须得关注一下你不会认表这件事了。"

我感觉自己的脸"刷"的一下红了。"用我的数字式手表，我就会认时间。"我说，"对了，我有些头疼。"

　　"别紧张。"爸爸说,"我们编了个小游戏来帮你。"

　　"就像寻宝游戏一样。"妈妈补充道。

　　"最后还有奖品哟!"安说。

　　"真的?"我说。听上去还蛮有意思的嘛!

21

爸爸说，关于认读时间，我还需要些提示。我们讨论了一些问题，这些问题我在学校里都学过。

安帮我画图。

之后妈妈教了我一条口诀：

短短指针威力大，现在几点全靠它。

这个太容易记了。"好吧。"我说，"我的第一张任务卡在哪里？"

分针

5 分钟

5 分钟

5 分钟

5 分钟

时针

每 5 分钟计 1 格

一个小时是 60 分钟

半个小时是 30 分钟

一刻钟是 15 分钟

长针指示分钟

短针指示小时

23

妈妈递给我一张卡片，我读了一下。

"我给你点提示吧……"安说。

"不用。"我说，"我自己可以完成！"

我开始盘算，时针指向7，说明是七点多钟。分针指向12，那就说明是7:00！并不难嘛！

每天早上7:00我在干什么呢？起床！第二张任务卡一定就在我的房间里！

可在我房间里的什么地方呢？哈哈！7:00，我还在床上呢！我把枕头挪开，下一张任务卡就在这里。

滴答滴答在计时！现在几点你可知？

好吧，时针指向7而分针指向1。我知道按照每5分钟1格来计算分钟。既然分针指向1，那就代表7:05。7:05我在干什么呢？

洗澡啊！我跑到浴室，在肥皂盒上发现了另一张任务卡。卡片黏糊糊的，可还能看清楚。

嗯，时针指向7而分针指向3，所以时间是7:15。我每天7:15都在刷牙。

没错，下一张任务卡就裹在我的牙刷上！

时针在 7 和 8 之间，分针指向 6，所以时间是7:30。
每天 7:30 我都在吃早饭。

越来越简单了！

又对了！

卡片就放在餐桌上。

钟表卡片并不难，想想谁总汪汪叫？

"僵尸！"我喊道，"7:45我要遛狗！"

僵尸一溜烟地跑进厨房，爸爸、妈妈和安紧跟在后边。

"祝贺你！"他们喊道。

　　我看到僵尸嘴里叼着个信封，里面竟是去看怪物电影马拉松的票！简直难以置信！我从没想到我还能去看这个！"太好啦！"我说。

我的数字式手表还是没有找到，但这已经不重要了。现在，不管什么样的钟表我都能看懂！

而且，就像我说过的，我再也没有迟到过，有时还会早到呢！

时 间

一小时是 60 分钟　　　半小时是 30 分钟　　　一刻钟是 15 分钟

分针

时针

4:00

4:30

4:15

多种时间表达法

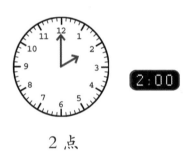

2:00

2 点

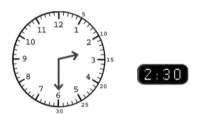

2:30

2 点半, 2 点 30 分

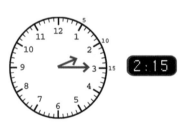

2:15

2 点 1 刻, 2 点 15 分

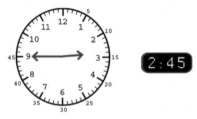

2:45

2 点 45 分, 2 点 3 刻, 差 1 刻 3 点

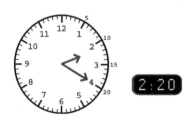

2:20

2 点 20 分

2:55

2 点 55 分, 差 5 分 3 点

亲爱的家长朋友，请您和孩子一起完成下面这些内容，会有更大的收获哟！

提高阅读能力

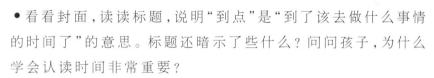

- 看看封面，读读标题，说明"到点"是"到了该去做什么事情的时间了"的意思。标题还暗示了些什么？问问孩子，为什么学会认读时间非常重要？
- 讨论一下封面的图画。麦克斯在做什么呢？让孩子猜一猜故事会怎样展开。
- 说一说关于时间的词语：迟到、早到、早晨、晚上、抓紧、等待、拖延、匆匆忙忙、快点、当……的时候、然后、钟、表、时刻表。让孩子用每个词语造个句子。
- 猜谜语：

  什么东西有两只手没有脚，却能一个星期跑上168个小时？（时钟）

巩固数学概念

- 利用第 32 页上的表盘做游戏,你说个时间,让孩子用另一种方式表达出来。

- 画个表盘,说出一个时间,让孩子指出 15 分钟后的时间。

- 仍然使用上述表盘,5 分钟 1 格地计时,数一圈至 1 小时。练习认读时间,准确到分。例如,将时钟指向 3.05,让孩子说出时间。再 1 分、2 分地走表,让孩子试着说出分钟的变化。

- 谈一谈"耗时"的问题。例如,麦克斯 7:00 起床,7:40 吃完早饭,他总共用了多长时间?

生活中的数学

- 帮助孩子按照其作息规律制作一张"晨事表"。在每项活动旁边画上表盘,让孩子在表盘上按照自己的实际情况画出时针和分针。再计算一下,做每件事都花了多长时间?

- 让孩子将自己的"晨事表"与麦克斯的相对照。例如,谁起得早?谁穿衣服耗时长?吃饭呢?等等。

向日葵花朵朵开,半点的花儿等你摘。

分针指向 6,时针刚走过数字几,就是几点半。

把相同时间的小蜗牛用线连起来。

今天麦克斯特别忙,请你根据钟面上的时间画出他的出行路线。

商 店

邮 局

图书馆

钟表店

艺术馆

亲爱的小朋友,你会认钟表了吗?像麦克斯一样制作一张自己的"时间表",让你的一天变得更加从容、有条理吧!

时　间	事　情

互动练习1：略

互动练习2：

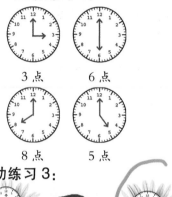

3点　　6点

8点　　5点

互动练习3：

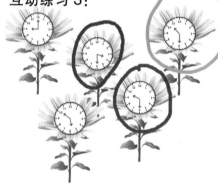

互动练习4：

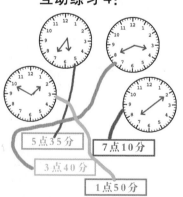

5点35分

7点10分

3点40分

1点50分

互动练习5：

互动练习6：

互动练习7：略

（习题设计：张　莹）

It's About Time, Max!

"Time to wake up, Max!" called my mom.

I yawned and checked my watch. Seven o'clock. I wake up at the same time every morning. Then I can do all the things I need to do before I catch the school bus at 8:05. I'm never late.

Every morning from 7:05 to 7:15 I take a shower.

From 7:15 to 7:20 I brush my teeth.

From 7:20 to 7:30 I get dressed.

From 7:30 to 7:45 I eat my Crispy Critters. Yum!

From 7:45 to 7:55 I walk my dog, Zombie.(I call him that 'cause I love monster movies!)

Then I go and wait for the bus. It comes at 8:05. Mrs. Dunn, the driver, is on time every day, just like me.

All right, all right. I have to admit that for a while I was really late. Here's how it started.

"Time to wake up, Max," my mom called.

I showered and brushed my teeth. I got dressed. Then I reached for my digital watch.

It wasn't on my night stand. Or in my bathrobe pocket, or on the sink! Oh no!

I tied my sneakers and ran downstairs.

"Hey,"I said. "Has anybody seen my watch?"

"Nope," said Mom and Dad.

"Nope," said my sister, Ann.

"What am I going to do?" I moaned.

"I have a watch you can borrow," said Ann.

"You'd better hurry up," said Mom. "It's already 7:50."

Uh-oh. I was five minutes behind schedule! I put on Ann's watch, called Zombie, and zoomed out the door.

When we got to the corner, I decided to check the time.

Yikes! It wasn't a digital watch. This one had hands on it!

What time was it? I couldn't tell. I ran home as fast as I could.

Oops. My mom was waiting outside with a not-very-happy look on her face."You just missed the bus!"she said.

So Mom had to drive me to school and write a late note. I was sooooo embarrassed.

The next day was Saturday. I was all excited because that afternoon I was going to my first surprise party ever. Dad was going to drive me.

He kept yawning. "In case I nod off, be sure to wake me at 5:30," he said. "We should leave then."

I stared at Dad. My parents are sort of old-fashioned. There wasn't a single digital clock in the house.

"Five-thirty?" I said, stalling.

"You know," said Dad, "when the big hand is on the 6 and the little hand is between the 5 and the 6?"He smiled.

That made it a little easier. "Okay," I said.

When the little hand was by the 6, and the big hand was on the 5, I woke up my dad. He wasn't very happy. Not at all.

"Max!" he said, "I asked you to wake me at 5:30. It's 6:25!"

I must have mixed up the hands. We drove straight to the party, but I missed the best part—when everyone jumps out and yells "SURPRISE!" What a bummer.

That Sunday afternoon Mom and I went to the movies to see *The Boy Who Ate Cleveland.* Like I said, I love monster movies. So does Mom.

We got to the mall early.

"I want to go to Jay's," I said. "He might have some new monster comics for me."

"And I want to go to the CD store," said Mom. "I'll meet you here at a quarter after three."

"Um... maybe I'll go with you," I said. Then I remembered that the comic book store had a big digital clock on the wall.

"Okay," I said, "a quarter after three is fine."

I looked at comic books for a while. Then, when the clock said a quarter after three, I went to meet my mom.

"Max, I've been waiting for ten minutes," Mom said. "The movie already started!"

"But I'm on time," I said. "It's a quarter after. A quarter is 25 cents, and it's 3:25."

"No, Max," Mom said. "An hour is 60 minutes. A quarter hour is 15 minutes. A quarter after three is 3:15, not 3:25."

So we missed the movie. I felt pretty bad.

That night Mom called me into the living room. The whole family was there. So were papers with clocks and numbers.

"Max," said Mom, "we couldn't help noticing that you can't tell time."

I felt myself turning red. "But I can tell time—on my digital watch," I said. "Besides, I have a headache."

"Relax," Dad said. "We've made up a little game to help you out."

"Like a treasure hunt," Mom added.

"With a prize at the end," Ann said.

"Yeah?" I said. This almost sounded like fun!

Dad said that I'd need a few hints about telling time. We talked about some stuff I think I had in school.

Ann drew pictures for me.

Then Mom told me this rhyme.

The little hand has all the power.
That is why it tells the hour.

That was easy to remember. "Okay," I said. "Where's my first clue?"

45

Mom handed me a card. I started to read it.

"I'll give you a hint—" said Ann.

"No," I said. "I can do it!"

I thought to myself. The hour hand was on 7, so that meant it was 7-something. And since the minute hand was on 12, it was 7 o'clock! This wasn't so hard!

So what do I do at 7 o'clock every morning? I wake up! The next clue must be in my room!

But where in my room? Ah-hah! At 7:00, I was in bed! I picked up my pillow and there was the next clue.

Okay. The little hand was on 7 and the big hand was on 1. I remembered how you count by fives to find the minutes. So, since the big hand was on 1, that meant it was five minutes after 7. What do I do at 7:05?

I take a shower! I ran to the bathroom. And there on the soap dish was another clue. It was a little soggy, but I could read it.

Hmmm. The little hand was on 7 and the big hand was on 3. So it was fifteen minutes after 7. I brush my teeth at 7:15.

Sure enough, the next clue was wrapped around my toothbrush!

The little hand was between 7 and 8. The big hand was on 6. So it was thirty minutes after 7. At 7:30 each day I eat my breakfast.

This was getting easier and easier!

Right again!

My clue was on the kitchen table.

"Zombie!" I yelled. "I walk Zombie at 7:45!"

Zombie came running into the kitchen. Mom, Dad, and Ann were close behind.

"Congratulations!" they shouted.

Then I saw an envelope in Zombie's mouth. Inside were tickets to the Monster Movie Marathon! I couldn't believe it! I never thought I'd get to go. "All right!" I said.

I never did find my digital watch—but that doesn't matter. Now I can tell time on all kinds of clocks.

And, as I said, I'm never late. Sometimes, I'm even early!